THE JA

Star Player Wanted

TOM WATT

RISING STARS

Rising Stars UK Ltd.
22 Grafton Street, London W1S 4EX
www.risingstars-uk.com

Text, design and layout © 2009 Rising Stars Uk Ltd.
The right of Tom Watt to be identified as the author of this work has been
asserted by him in accordance with the Copyright, Design and Patents Act,
1988.

Published 2009

Publisher: Gill Budgell
Editor: Jane Wood
Text design and typesetting: Clive Sutherland
Illustrator: Michael Emmerson for Advocate Art
Cover design: Burville-Riley Partnership
Cover photograph: Ron Coello at www.coellophotography.co.uk
With special thanks to; Robert Dye, Harry Garner, Tyrone Smith, Lewis
McKenzie, Kobina Crankson and Alex Whyte

British Library Cataloguing in Publication Data.
A CIP record for this book is available from the British Library.

ISBN: 978-1-84680-481-6

Printed in the UK by CPI Bookmarque, Croydon, CR0 4TD

Contents

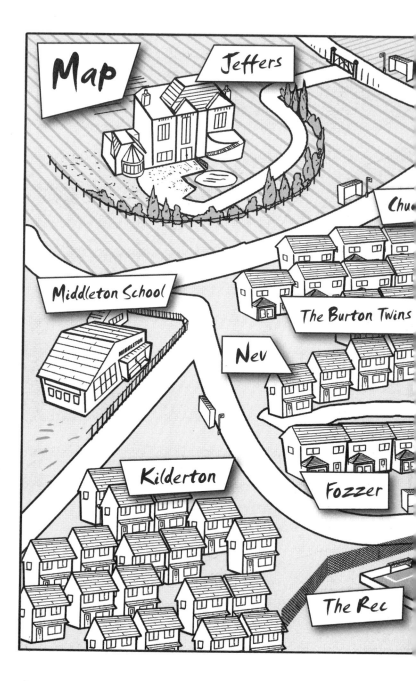

Map

Jeffers

Chu

Middleton School

The Burton Twins

Nev

Kilderton

Fozzer

The Rec

4

Upton Prep School

The Vale

rk

Keeps

Dev

Valley Road Stadium

Parkside School

PARKSIDE

5

Meet the Jags

Andy

Name: Andrew Burton

Fact: He's the Jags' captain.

Loves: Spurs

FYI: The Jags may be his mates, but they'd better not forget he's the Skipper.

Burts

Name: Terry Burton

Fact: He's Andy's twin brother.

Loves: Football, football, and more football. He's football crazy!

FYI: He's a big Arsenal fan.

Dev

Name: Ryan Devlin

Fact: He's very forgetful.

Loves: Daydreaming!

FYI: He's always covered in mud and bruises.

Fozzer

Name: Hamed Foster

Fact: He can run like crazy, but he shoots like crazy too – sometimes at the wrong goal!

Loves: Telling bad jokes.

FYI: His best friend is Nev.

Keeps

Name: Jim Ward

Fact: He's the Jags' Number One goalie – whether he likes it or not!

Loves: Trying to score from his end of the pitch.

FYI: He's the tallest member of the Jags.

Jeffers

Name: Jeffrey Gilfoyle Chapman

Fact: He's the only one of the Jags who doesn't live on the Chudley Park estate.

Loves: Being in the Jags.

FYI: He's the Jags' top goal-scorer.

Nev

Name: Denton Neville

Fact: Nev is the Jags' most talented player.

Loves: Fozzer's bad jokes.

FYI: He keeps his feet on the ground and always looks out for his football crazy mates.

Mrs Burton

Name: Pam Burton

Fact: The Burton twins' mum, and a team 'mum' for all the Jags.

Loves: Sorting out her boys.

FYI: Doesn't actually like football!

Mr Ward

Name: Jack Ward

Fact: He's Jim's dad and the Jags' coach!

Loves: Going on and on, doing his team talks.

FYI: He's taking his coaching exams.

The New Boy

Playing for the Jags is so much fun. They're a good team and Nev is a very good player.

Nev   Hey, Jeffers! You're early for training tonight. Nobody else is here yet.

Jeffers   I came straight from school.
If I go home, my mother won't
let me out again until I've done
all my homework!

Nev   Good thinking. Let's play until
the others get here.

Jeffers   Sure. What shall we do?

Nev   Let's see how many keepy-ups we can do.

Jeffers   Yeah, like the subs you see on TV. You see them doing keepy-ups at half-time.

Nev   All right then, Jeffers. On your head.

Jeffers   That's 20 between us! Not bad!

Nev   Not bad at all. Where did you learn to play?

Jeffers   I could ask you the same thing, Denton.

Nev   "Denton"? When you say it like that, you sound like my dad when he's telling me off! Call me Nev. Everybody else does.

Jeffers   Okay, Nev.

Nev   That's better. I don't know where Andy found you. But you're part of the Jags now. We can always do with good players like you, Jeffers.

Jeffers   Thanks, Denton. Um, I mean, Nev. Look. Here come the others.

Hot Gossip!

We trained for an hour. Mr Ward made us do one-twos. He said that's how the pros do it. At the end, he said there might be some pros at the game on Sunday. But he didn't say who ...

Nev   Jeffers, are you getting the bus?

Jeffers Yes, there's one at half past.

Nev   Well, wait for me. I'll walk to the
                    bus stop with you.

Jeffers   How long have you known
                    Mr Ward, Nev?

Nev   Oh, ages. He set up the Jags in
                    the first place. Why?

Jeffers   Oh, just sometimes I find it hard
to get what he's saying.

Nev   Don't worry about that, mate.
We've been with him for years
and we still don't get it half the
time.

Jeffers   I really like him. And he's a
good coach. But …

Nev   But he's a bit mad, too? Well, that's what you get if you think you're Alex Ferguson. He works at Vale United, you know. He's the kit man. I think he used to play for them, too.

Jeffers   What did he mean when he said there might be some pros at the game on Sunday? I mean, who are we playing?

Nev   We're playing Brook. Don't
             worry, they aren't pros. I bet
             you score a hat-trick against
             them.

Jeffers So who does Mr Ward mean,
             Nev?

Nev   I don't know. I tell you what, I'll
             call in on the Burtons on the
             way home. If they don't know,
             I bet their mum will.

Jeffers Does Mrs Burton work for Vale United as well?

Nev No. But she works hard for the Jags. She drives us round, washes our kit, makes us squash and cakes. And she usually knows what's going on.

Jeffers I'm glad somebody does! Look! There's my bus! See you, Nev!

Nev Yeah, let's meet at the Rec tomorrow. See you!

Local Talent

Well, the next day I went to the Rec to meet Nev. I had to know what was going on. Who were the pros? Had Nev got the gossip?

Nev   Hi, Jeffers! I wasn't sure if you'd come or not. It's not a training night, after all.

Jeffers   No, but I've brought a ball, just in case. Where are the others?

Nev   Probably watching TV. Or just late. I told them to meet us here.

Jeffers   What time did you tell them to get here?

Nev   Ah. I didn't tell them that. How did you know what time to arrive?

Jeffers   I didn't. I just came straight from school again.

Nev   Where's that ball, then? Have you got any new tricks?

Jeffers   I'll show you a new trick if you'll tell me what's going on.

Nev   Okay. Well, Mrs Burton thinks it might be someone from a big club. He might be at the game on Sunday.

Jeffers   Which big club? Who? Why?

Nev   How many questions is that?

Jeffers   Come on, Nev.

Nev   Well, it seems Mr Ward knows
somebody who knows
somebody. And they are going
to send *another* somebody to one
of our games!

Jeffers   Do you mean a scout? A Premier
League scout? Which club?

Nev   Well, that's how it sounds to me, but Mrs Burton said she didn't know. She isn't really sure about any of it.

Jeffers   Well, we'll find out on Sunday, I suppose. What did Andy and Burts think?

Nev   Well, you know what Burts is like. He thinks the scout will come with the England manager.

Jeffers   The England manager? Burts is crazy. What did Andy say?

Nev   He said Burts was crazy. And he also said not to tell you about the scout.

Jeffers   What? Why not?

Nev   Hang on a minute, Jeffers. Pass me that ball.

Who's on the List?

I know it was driving Jeffers crazy. But I wanted him to show me that new trick. And the best way to do that was to keep him hanging on for more gossip about Sunday and the scout.

Jeffers   So, why didn't Andy want you to tell me?

Nev   In a minute. Just show me that trick first. So, it's like a Ronaldo step-over?

Jeffers   Yes. But then you flick it up in the air, like this.

Nev   That's really cool. Who did you see doing this?

Jeffers I can't remember his name.
A Spanish player. He was
playing against Real Madrid.
I saw it on TV.

Nev Step over. Step over. And then
flick it up in the air.

Jeffers   That's it. And then you can shoot or pass on the volley.

Nev   That's really cool, Jeffers. No wonder Andy doesn't want you to know about the scout.

Jeffers   Come on, Nev. We had a deal. I showed you the trick. Now tell me what Andy said about the scout.

Nev   Well, Burts and Andy think the scout is coming to watch one player. One very good player.

Jeffers   Yes. You, probably. You're the best player we've got.

Nev   No. They think it's you. We've never had a scout at one of our games before. Then you start playing for us. And the next thing is, there's a scout coming.

Jeffers   But why didn't they want you to tell me about the scout?

Nev   Andy thinks that if you know there's a scout there, you'll do all your tricks. And then you might leave the Jags if you get spotted.

Jeffers   Me? Leave the Jags? But I've only just joined. Andy knows that. He got me on the team.

Nev   Well, we'll see what happens on Sunday. I'm off home for my tea.

Spotted!

The game on Sunday was a lot harder than anybody thought. The Brook team had a new keeper who saved all our shots. But then, right at the end, Fozzer passed the ball up the wing to me ...

Nev   Cross it, Jeffers! Cross it!

Jeffers   Near post, Nev!

Nev   Got it!

Jeffers   Goaaaaal!

Nev   Great cross, Jeffers!

Jeffers   Great header, Nev. The keeper had no chance!

Nev   I wonder if that scout is still here.

Jeffers The scout? I forgot all about him.

Nev   Yeah. If he's gone, he missed a good goal. Let's make sure Brook don't get one back, eh?

Jeffers Full-time! That's 1–0!

Nev Come on the Jags! Man of the match, Jeffers!

Jeffers Thanks, Nev. But no sign of the scout.

Nev Yes, there is. Look. Who's that, talking to Mr Ward?

We all stood and watched. Mr Ward shook hands with the man and he left. Then, he came over to talk to the Jags ...

Nev   Well, what a fuss all that was, eh, Jeffers?

Jeffers   What? I didn't hear what Mr Ward said.

Nev   I think the Burton twins got a bit carried away. That man was a pro all right. And he was from the F.A.

Jeffers   Great. What did he say?

Nev   He thought we did very well.

Jeffers   Who was he watching?

Nev   Nobody. Well, I mean, everybody. He's a coach, not a scout. And he came to see Mr Ward, not us. About Mr Ward's coaching badges.

Jeffers Do you know something? I'm glad.

Nev Eh?

Jeffers I don't care about gossip and scouts and star players and secrets. All I care about is playing for the Jags.

Nev Me too, Jeffers. Got any new tricks?

Jeffers   Have a go at this. You can try it
              in next week's game!

Nev   Yeah! You never know who
              might be watching!

Nev and   Come on the Jags!
Jeffers

MANCHESTER UNITED 1
CHELSEA 1

I love playing for the Jags. I love watching football as well. After our game against Brook, Nev asked me round to his house to watch Manchester United against Chelsea on TV.

Jeffers   Look at those step-overs, Nev.

Nev   Yeah. They were almost as good as yours! But Man United have still won the ball.

Jeffers   Oh, he's scored on the volley!
That's 1–0 to United.

Nev   Now Chelsea need someone to
get into the area. That's it!
What a shot! That's 1–all. That
will be goal of the season!

The Coach

Mr Ward has been doing his coaching badges. That means he is learning how to be a better coach. The man from the F.A. wanted to see how he was getting on with his coaching badges.

Every team needs a good coach. The coach keeps the players fit and helps them to play better as a team.

 Some coaches are managers, too, like
Sir Alex Ferguson and Arsene Wenger.
The manager picks the team and
decides which position everyone will
play in. The manager decides when to
send on the subs as well. It's a very
important job.

The Coach Quiz

Questions

1 Who is the Jags' coach?

2 What did the man from the F.A. want?

3 What does a coach do?

4 What does a manager do?

Answers

1 Mr Ward.

2 To see how Mr Ward was getting on with his coaching badges.

3 Keeps the players fit and helps them to play better as a team.

4 Picks the team, decides which position everyone will play in, and sends on the subs.

About the Author

Tom Watt, who wrote the Jags books, used to manage a football team. His team played to raise money for charity. They were called the Walford Boys' Club.

Tom used to fix up all the games. He got the kit for the players to wear. He made sure everybody got to the games on time. But Tom really liked being the manager so he could pick the team. Then he could always put himself on the team!

THE JAGS

RISING STARS

The Jags books are available from most book sellers.
For mail order information
please call Rising Stars on 0871 47 23 01 0
or visit www.risingstars-uk.com